BOOKSHOP
Phonics
Partner Practice Book

MONDO
PUBLISHING

For information contact:

MONDO Publishing
980 Avenue of the Americas
New York, NY 10018

Visit our website at www.mondopub.com

Printed in China

09 10 11 12   9 8 7 6 5 4 3 2

ISBN 1-60201-134-6
ISBN 978-1-60201-134-2

Designed by Witz End Design

Contents

Say the Names

a   A   a   a

A   a   A   a

Say and Write

Aa

Say the Names

T	a	t	A
a	t	A	T
t	A	t	T

Say and Write

T t

Say the Names

M	T	m	a
t	A	M	t
a	T	a	m

Say and Write

M m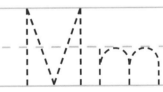

Say the Names

A	s	m	S
T	a	S	M
S	t	s	M

Say and Write

S s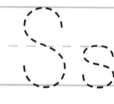

© Mondo Publishing 2007

Use with Lesson 7.

Say the Names

a	F	M	F
S	m	f	T
F	t	s	F
t	F	A	m

Say and Write

Ff

Name _____

Say the Names

M	p	f	P
a	T	p	S
P	A	t	F
t	m	s	a

☐

Say and Write

Pp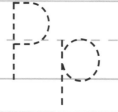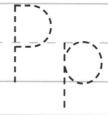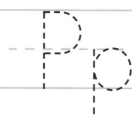

☐

Say the Names

I   s   T   i   F

S   i   A   m   t

P   M   I   f   a

t   s   F   p   I

Say and Write

Ii Ii Ii Ii Ii Ii Ii

Name _____

Say the Names

N   A   m   N   P

M   t   n   i   F

p   N   a   f   S

I   F   S   a   T

Say and Write

Nn   Nn   Nn   Nn

© Mondo Publishing 2007

Use with Lesson 13.

Say the Names

N	d	P	i	D
I	s	D	M	S
a	n	t	f	D
F	T	m	A	p

Say and Write

D d

Name _____

Say the Names

O	P	d	N	o
F	t	O	i	m
I	o	n	D	A
d	f	a	s	d

☐

Say and Write

  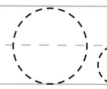

☐

Say the Names

s	L	t	a	O
n	D	M	l	S
F	d	L	p	l
o	i	N	d	I

Say and Write

L l

Name _____

Say the Names

O	R	s	N	R
F	a	I	R	T
d	T	o	L	M
I	f	r	P	D

Say and Write

Rr R̶r̶ R̶r̶ R̶r̶ R̶r̶

Use with Lessons 19 and 20.

Say the Names

h	r	t	H	F
N	d	h	i	R
l	H	P	s	n
O	m	a	r	d

Say and Write

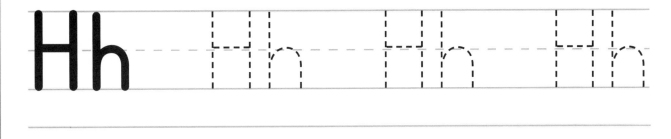

Name _____

Say the Names

R	e	s	E	D
F	P	E	b	I
M	H	h	l	m
r	b	o	n	e

Say and Write

E e

Use with Lesson 23.

Say the Names

N	L	r	H	B
b	F	B	o	D
A	m	s	n	r
t	p	I	b	e

Say and Write

Bb

Say the Names

u	S	D	d	T
e	U	m	u	L
H	b	r	b	H
d	n	U	O	D

Say and Write

Say the Names

g   O   i   G   l

R   U   g   E   D

P   G   h   T   g

d   n   r   b   N

Say and Write

Gg   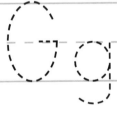 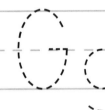

Name _____

Say the Names

h	C	U	c	A
c	g	E	t	R
F	M	D	h	d
a	n	b	C	s

Say and Write

C c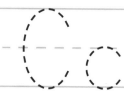

Use with Lessons 29 and 30.

Say the Names

U	D	c	g	C
H	e	P	f	o
i	G	u	B	n

Look and Say Words

the	a	see	the
see	the	a	see

Read the Sentence

See the  .

Say the Names

a   B   u   f   e

s   R   m   I   T

P   C   n   L   G

Sound and Say Word

at

Look and Say Words

see   the   a   see

a   see   see   the

Read the Sentence

See a  .

Name _____

Say the Names

C	s	F	h	o
t	A	b	D	L
M	E	r	u	G

Sound and Say Words

am   mat   at

Look and Say Words

I	on	happy	I
the	happy	a	see
see	the	I	on

Read the Sentence

I see a happy  .

Say the Names

B	E	G	p	I
D	h	T	a	R
N	i	C	u	O

Sound and Say Words

at	Sam	mat	sat
am	mat	at	Sam

Look and Say Words

happy	on	see	I
a	the	a	happy
on	see	I	the

Read the Sentence

I am on the mat.

Use with Lessons 39 and 40.

Say the Names

U	O	s	N	h
b	F	I	P	M
D	r	g	I	E

Sound and Say Words

mat	at	fat	fast
Sam	fast	am	sat

Look and Say Words

I	is	cat	my
happy	cat	the	a
see	my	is	on

Read the Sentence

Sam is my cat.

Name _____

Say the Names

H	S	e	a	T
M	C	g	d	B
N	f	U	i	P

Sound and Say Words

map   Sam   fat   am

fast   at   maps   sat

Look and Say Words

the   is   my   cat

happy   see   a   on

cat   my   I   is

Read the Sentence

My cat is on the map.

Say the Names

O E v a V

U v L h r

C g b V D ☐

Sound and Say Words

map am map fat

at mat sat fast ☐

Look and Say Words

little is big happy

my a we on

we big little see ☐

Read the Sentences

1. Sam sat on the little mat.

2. We see a big cat. ☐

Name _____

Say the Names

G   j   V   M   u

s   I   J   t   p

J   c   n   j   F

Sound and Say Words

mat   am   map   fat

fast   at   fast   sat

Look and Say Words

little   big   we   I

happy   the   cat   see

on   we   little   is

Read the Sentences

1. I see the big map.
2. Sam is happy.

Use with Lessons 49 and 50.

Say the Names

e	H	k	g	K
B	k	V	D	J

Sound and Say Words

fat	map	tap	am
mat	at	maps	fast
fat	sat	pat	Pam

Look and Say Words

and	little	very	look
my	we	see	happy
very	look	and	the

Read the Sentences

1. Pam is little and fast.
2. Sam and Pat look happy.

Say the Names

W   s   U   M   w

v   j   w   c   g

Sound and Say Words

pat	mat	Pam	map
am	maps	sat	fast
at	Sam	maps	tap

Look and Say Words

look	little	very	and
is	we	my	happy
on	very	see	look

Read the Sentences

1. We see the map.
2. Pam sat on the mat.

Say the Names

H	V	r	j	K
D	w	I	P	c

Sound and Say Words

pit	Tim	it	mitt
fit	sat	Pam	sit
miss	if	map	tip

Look and Say Words

here	we	my	this
can	on	this	is
look	here	very	can

Read the Sentences

1. Look! Tim is here.
2. This is a big mitt.

Say the Names

J   W   v   U   g

C   B   m   P   n

Sound and Say Words

an	nap	if	ant
fan	map	it	naps
pan	tan	sit	man

Look and Say Words

this	is	and	can
my	very	here	on
here	this	big	look

Read the Sentences

1. A big ant is in here!
2. I can sit on this.

Say the Names

J   o   y   D   R

n   W   h   v   Y

Sound and Say Words

an   it   fast   pin

mitt   fist   in   ant

fat   Tim   fit   pit

Look and Say Words

and   to   are   this

to   like   my   here

little   look   we   like

Read the Sentences

1. The little ant is on Tim.
2. I like to nap on the mat.

Say the Names

Y   b   q   C   V

Q   U   g   W   q

Sound and Say Words

Pam	an	fin	pan
fan	tin	am	ant
sit	man	Tim	if

Look and Say Words

this	like	and	to
are	on	look	are
to	like	here	very

Read the Sentences

1. I like my fat cat Sam.
2. Look at the big man.

© Mondo Publishing 2007

Use with Lessons 64 and 65.

Say the Name

y x J X p
Q S x M w

☐

Sound and Say Words

it   tap   tip   fan

pan   if   sit   map

Tim   ant   man   fit

☐

Look and Say Words

you   are   come   put

like   put   this   you

come   look   here   to

☐

Read the Sentences

1. We are very fast.
2. Come here and sit on the mat.

☐

Name _____

Say the Names

z   W   X   y   d

Q   O   Z   r   z

Sound and Say Words

sit	Tim	fit	ant
pan	fin	nap	in
sat	miss	man	fast

Look and Say Words

come	look	you	like
put	and	this	you
here	are	to	come

Read the Sentences

1. We like to nap.
2. Put the cat on the mat.

Say the Names

X   q   H   z   k

w   V   J   c   Y   ☐

Sound and Say Words

pad   Dan   dip   Dad

sand   did   fast   sits   ☐

Look and Say Words

put   do   to   with

do   you   want   come

want   you   are   happy   ☐

Read the Sentences

1. Do you want to come with me?
2. We want to sit with Dad.
3. Dan sits in the sand. ☐

Name _____

Say the Names

y   M   W   q   n

P   z   I   X   d

Sound and Say Words

mom   nod   pot   toss

on   fan   did   mop

Look and Say Words

down   want   to   from

do   we   are   here

come   put   want   with

Read the Sentences

1. Mom and Dan want to mop.
2. We sit with Mom and Dad.
3. Do you want to come with me?

Name _____

Say the Names

R   k   Y   b   C

U   g   W   Q   X ☐

Sound and Say Words

doll   lip   list   lap

land   lamp   lost   last ☐

Look and Say Words

my   put   with   come

play   down   you   here

said   are   this   want ☐

Read the Sentences

1. "I lost my doll," said Pam.
2. Sit down on the mat.
3. "The lamp is on," said Mom.

☐

Name _____

Say the Names

Y	U	g	k	I
C	Q	b	j	Z

Sound and Say Words

ran	rip	last	Ron
not	rat	miss	lift

Look and Say Words

said	do	put	down
play	my	want	like
said	little	you	with

Read the Sentences

1. "The cat ran very fast!" said Mom.

2. Do you want to play with my doll?

3. Ron and Tim like to play in the sand.

Sound and Say Words

hop	hill	hams	pond
hat	doll	sit	in
hid	tops	hot	lot

Look and Say Words

to	of	have	been
here	have	like	this
been	here	do	of
said	play	down	want

Read the Sentences

1. I have been to the pond.
2. We have a lot of hats.
3. Sam and Tim play on the hill.

Sound and Say Words

Ted	ran	pet	red
not	did	ram	on
net	let	help	rest

Look and Say Words

of	my	have	I
is	have	been	said
been	happy	of	down

Read the Sentences

1. Ed and Ted pet the ram.
2. I fell down the hill.
3. Let him tell the rest.

Sound and Say Words

end	bell	did	nap
sit	ant	best	hill
top	bats	ran	bad

Look and Say Words

were	play	they	been
said	has	down	of
has	to	were	they

Read the Story

Bats were at the top of the hill. They were very big. They were fast.

I want to see the bats. I am at the top of the hill. I see the bats. I am happy.

Sound and Say Words

pup	Pam	best	fun
run	fast	nut	lost
help	top	mud	red

Look and Say Words

they	has	come	were
big	look	they	is
little	were	my	has

Read the Story

Ed has a big pup. Pam has a little pup. Ed and Pam are best pals. The pups are best pals.

Ed, Pam, and the pups like to run. They like to run in the sun. They have a lot of fun.

Sound and Say Words

us	pond	hills	mud
red	bug	fun	gets
at	in	lot	bad

Look and Say Words

does	play	to	the
any	said	you	play
come	we	does	any

Read the Story

Ann and Ron run to the pond. They like to play in the mud. They want to see a lot of bugs.

"I do not see any bugs," said Ron.

"I see a lot of bugs. Come here and look!" said Ann.

Sound and Say Words

sick	let	bag	fills
list	pond	mud	well
ram	not	hill	get

Look and Say Words

any	big	play	does
little	look	any	this
I	does	here	play

Read the Story

Ted is sick. Ted must sit and rest. Ron and Sam come to see Ted. "We want to play with you," they said.

Ted gets well. Ron and Sam come and play with Ted. They play and have a lot of fun. They are very happy.

Sound and Say Words

van	hen	pill	sled
let	slid	hop	mess
gas	luck	vet	slip

Look and Say Words

was	been	put	who
there	who	happy	are
said	with	was	there

Read the Story

Ted and I like to play. We like to play in the sand. We like to run in the sun.

The sand is very hot. Ted hops on the sand. I hop on the sand. We are happy in the sun.

Sound and Say Words

jump	pick	sun	slid
lamp	jog	met	help
sled	just	slim	tells

Look and Say Words

there	you	we	was
come	is	there	who
was	who	my	little

Read the Story

There is a little dog who likes to jump. He is Jill's little dog. He jumps up and down. The dog bumps a cup of jam. It makes a big mess. The dog is sad.

"Do not be sad," Jill tells the dog. "I will fix the mess." Jill hugs the little dog.

Sound and Say Words

stop	desk	jump	leg
pig	bell	kids	ten
Ken	ask	step	mom

Look and Say Words

into	any	your	good
does	who	into	your
play	good	there	was

Read the Story

Jack sits at the desk. A little bug jumps on the desk.

"Jump on my hand," Jack said. "I will put you in the grass."

The little bug jumps on Jack's hand. Jack puts the bug in the grass. The little bug is happy.

Sound and Say Words

wet	duck	had	well
dug	mops	went	just
sun	smack	with	stop

Look and Say Words

into	said	to	your
good	down	into	of
have	your	the	good

Read the Story

Ten little ducks ran up the hill. They slid in the wet grass. They fell down into a big pit. *Smack!*

"We are stuck!" they said.

"Come, come," said Mom Duck.

The ten little ducks went with Mom Duck. They were happy.

Sound and Say Words

fish	kid	end	shell
still	wish	shop	pet
its	Tom	fins	went

Look and Say Words

find	now	has	saw
like	saw	find	my
here	look	little	now

Read the Story

Tom wants a pet fish. Tom and Dad go to the pet shop.

"Let's find a fish that has big, red fins," said Tom.

"Like this fish?" asks Dad.

"Yes! I want that fish," said Tom. Tom and Dad get the fish.

Sound and Say Words

yell	shop	ask	fish
if	went	yes	step
wish	did	spill	pet

Look and Say Words

said	any	saw	now
find	now	who	does
there	saw	play	find

Read the Story

"Can you come and play in the sand with me?" asks Matt.

"Yes, I can," said Jack. "Let's go."

Matt and Jack find a stick in the sand.

"Let's dig!" said Matt. Matt and Jack dig a big pit.

Sound and Say Words

spot	quick	shell	yes
help	got	will	Deb
rip	vet	quack	ship

Look and Say Words

her	does	now	our
said	as	your	her
very	our	put	as

Read the Story

Deb is sad. Her duck does not quack. Deb and her duck go to the vet.

"She must rest. If she gets rest, she will quack," said the vet.

Deb lets her duck nap and nap. Now her duck can quack. "Quack, quack," said her duck.

Sound and Say Words

Stan	next	fits	dog
fish	jog	box	lot
fox	get	rug	hen

Look and Say Words

as	have	our	do
her	of	you	her
like	our	we	as

Read the Story

Stan has a job at a pet shop. He has a fish in a dish. He has a fox in a box. He has a hen in a pen.

Kim went to the shop.

"Do you want a fox in a box?" said Stan.

"I want a hen in a pen," said Kim. Stan sells Kim the hen in a pen.

Use with Lessons 114 and 115.

Sound and Say Words

then	pack	dish	spin
luck	kiss	this	hot
with	quick	nest	asks

Look and Say Words

his	as	many	under
our	under	want	any
many	her	like	his

Read the Story

"I have bad luck," said Sam. He left his best box of rocks on the bus.

A man on the bus got Sam's box. The man saw Sam at the next stop.

"Is this your box of rocks?" said the man.

"Yes," said Sam. "This is my box!"

Sound and Say Words

math	back	stop	buzz
beg	just	den	ax
hat	than	zap	yell

Look and Say Words

many	good	his	under
saw	your	now	many
under	his	into	find

Read the Story

Zack the rat smells a big yam. The yam is in a box on the desk.

Zack zips to the desk. He jumps in the box. There is the yam!

He gulps it down and licks his lips. Zack is fat and happy now.

Sound and Say Words

jump	step	such	yes
chop	hen	job	went
slam	box	tell	bath

Look and Say Words

about	said	yellow	one
down	have	the	about
yellow	one	to	of

Read the Story

Zack has a pet chimp. The chimp likes to sit on a yellow box. He likes to chat with Zack.

Zack wants the chimp to have a bath. The chimp does not want a bath. The chimp wants to chat and play.

"You are such a mess!" said Zack.

Sound and Say Words

not	glad	clip	zip
fish	chip	miss	big
must	hill	got	lunch

Look and Say Words

yellow	about	look	many
our	little	one	about
one	here	yellow	this

Read the Story

The class has lost its pet rabbit.

"We must find it. Quick! Look under your desks now!" Miss Black tells the class.

"We do not see it," yells the class.

"Stop! I see him," yells Max. "He is under that clock."

Miss Black puts the rabbit back in its box. The class is very glad.

Sound and Say Words

block	wet	help	made
same	late	mad	same
hen	stick	blame	take

Look and Say Words

was	some	about	two
funny	there	does	some
two	funny	play	who

Read the Story

"I want to bake a cake," said Mom. "Do you want to help me?"

"Yes. We do!" said Jane and Dan.

"Jane, you put in the cake mix. Dan, you can put two eggs in the mix. I will get the milk."

Mom puts the cake mix in the pan. The cake smells good. Yum!

Sound and Say Words

pet	way	left	end
tail	when	game	bake
glad	pain	back	pay

Look and Say Words

some	now	under	two
your	funny	find	some
two	one	many	funny

Read the Story

Pam got a game in the mail. "Look, Max! This came in the mail."

"Two can play this game," said Max. "May I play with you?"

Pam and Max play the game.

"This is a funny game," said Pam.

"I am sad this game has to end," said Max.

Use with Lessons 129 and 130.

Sound and Say Words

ride	safe	mix	Pam
on	that	bike	dig
much	crash	name	slide

Look and Say Words

from	said	other	three
pretty	down	yellow	have
three	other	about	pretty

Read the Story

Mike likes to ride his bike. He likes to ride in the sun.

One day Mike went to see Josh. On his way, the rain came down fast. His bike slid in the rain. *Crash!* Mike and his bike fell in the mud.

Josh ran to help Mike. "I am fine," Mike said. "Dad can fix my bike."

Sound and Say Words

mine	cry	say	ship
fly	rain	box	gave
cross	champ	tie	brush

Look and Say Words

other	pretty	we	three
you	little	look	come
other	my	three	pretty

Read the Story

Jeff has three cats. Jake and Jack are big and brave. The other cat, Blush, is soft and shy. Jake and Jack like to make Blush cry.

One day a big rat ran by. The brave cats hid. Shy Blush got the rat. It was a fine day.

Use with Lessons 134 and 135.

Sound and Say Words

gray	rope	way	ate
make	such	grin	rose
jump	went	poke	box

Look and Say Words

four	with	give	soon
has	were	four	they
give	soon	his	see

Read the Story

Rose has a little dog. The dog jumps in a hole. He cannot get up.

Rose has a rope to get the dog. She takes the rope and puts it down in the hole. Soon the dog is with Rose.

"Do not jump back in that hole!" yells Rose. "I am so glad you are safe now."

Sound and Say Words

day	take	pie	trap
hide	try	grab	goat
ask	road	coat	time

Look and Say Words

saw	soon	yellow	give
our	as	four	about
four	give	many	soon

Read the Story

Four goats want to chomp on grass. The best grass is at the top of the big hill.

The goats get to the top of the hill. They do not see the grass!

The grass is under a bunch of rocks. The goats dig and dig so they can get to the grass. At last, the happy goats chomp on the grass.

Sound and Say Words

wheel	drive	bend	neat
which	queen	smell	will
lift	wet	seat	hop

Look and Say Words

what	happy	here	again
soon	know	what	does
there	again	find	know

Read the Story

Queen Joan has a lot of roses.

"I like to smell the roses," said Queen Joan. "The buds smell good."

The leaves on the roses are lush and green. A bug jumps on a green leaf. He is about to munch on a leaf when Queen Joan yells.

"No, no!" yells Queen Joan. "Get off my roses!"

Sound and Say Words

eve	boat	grand	dress
say	much	Steve	club
fast	when	made	each

☐

Look and Say Words

know	down	again	said
have	they	from	what
again	what	been	know

☐

Read the Story

Drip. Drop. Drip. Drop. The rain does not stop. Steve and Pete want to play in the sun.

Drip. Drop. Drip. Drop. The rain falls again.

Drip. Drop. Drip. Drop. The rain does not stop for many days. Steve and Pete will stay home and play games.

☐

Use with Lessons 144 and 145.

Sound and Say Words

fell	need	dig	that
came	flip	clock	step
spot	green	not	desk

Look and Say Words

please	soon	many	away
her	funny	would	please
would	give	away	other

Read the Story

Luke wants to play in the band.

"Do you want to play a flute?" Mom asks. "Do you want to play the drums?"

"I would like to try the sax," Luke tells Mom. "I will try my best."

"I will get you a sax," Mom tells Luke. "One day you will play a fine tune in the band."

Sound and Say Words

glad	eat	doll	cute
cry	quack	clue	drop
stone	vet	gift	Pete

Look and Say Words

would	away	three	please
good	under	find	away
please	would	two	other

Read the Story

June and Pete are on a boat. They like to dive into the deep blue sea. They put on their swimsuits.

They can see fish and shells. They would like to take a fish home. But the fish swim away. June and Pete swim back to the boat.

Sound and Say Words

fish	then	start	coat
hen	part	say	try
white	game	line	barn

Look and Say Words

brown	I'm	come	there
into	their	find	I'm
your	now	brown	their

Read the Story

Jan and Jack get on a train. They take the train to a farm.

The farm has a big red barn. There are red hens and pink pigs in the barn.

Jan gets eggs from the red hens. Jack feeds the pink pigs.

Jack and Jan have a good time on the farm.

Sound and Say Words

far	goat	mine	eat
shot	cake	tube	tree
job	chip	home	keep

Look and Say Words

I'm	they	their	brown
down	been	I'm	many
their	brown	saw	our

Read the Story

I have a little brown goat. But it is not a good goat.

My goat likes to eat my stuff. It will eat my socks. It will eat my pants. It will eat my hats.

I'm happy to have a goat, but I do not like it when he eats my stuff.

Use with Lessons 154 and 155.

Sound and Say Words

dark	corn	thin	quick
team	drain	port	next
fork	hill	arm	yes

Look and Say Words

brown	please	know	funny
yellow	under	as	find
into	was	does	you

Read the Story

Tim has a fort in his backyard. It is in the big tree. The fort is for his pals. His pals like to come and play in his fort.

When it gets dark, Tim and his pals look at the stars. Tim likes his fort in the tree.

Sound and Say Words

that	grin	dress	keep
well	time	road	car
came	black	for	part

☐

Look and Say Words

their	would	again	give
other	some	about	his
her	now	your	who

☐

Read the Story

Kate and Sue like to jump rope.

"One, two, three! No one jumps as fast as me!" yells Kate as she jumps.

Sue smiles and yells back, "One, two, three, four! I can jump as fast as you!"

"Pretty soon it will be dark," Kate tells Sue. "It is time to go home."

☐

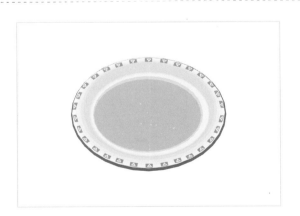

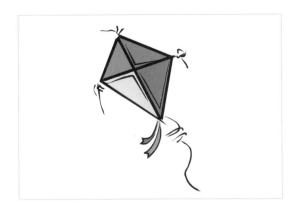

 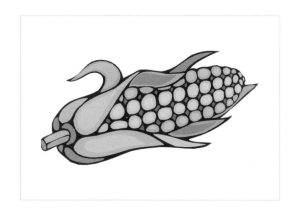

c

p

f

d

r

h

b

m

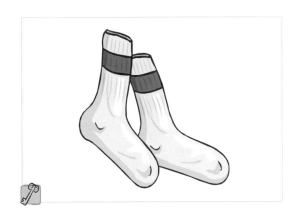

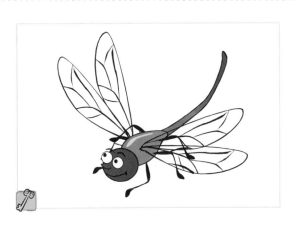

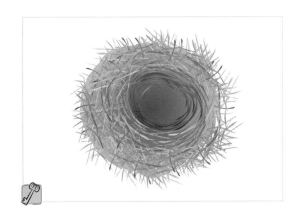

sh

_ck

a

a_e

s

t

n

i

l

o

e

z

u

v

j

g

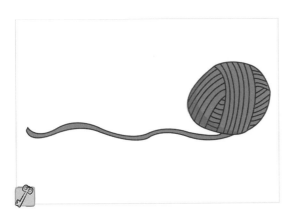

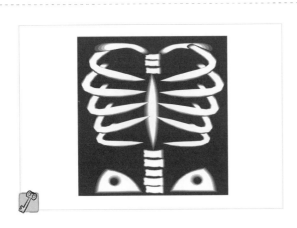

w

k

qu

y

th

x

ea

ch

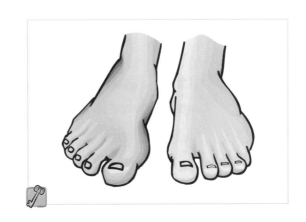

ay

ai

ie

i_e

o_e

_y

ee

oa

u_e

e_e

ar

ui

or

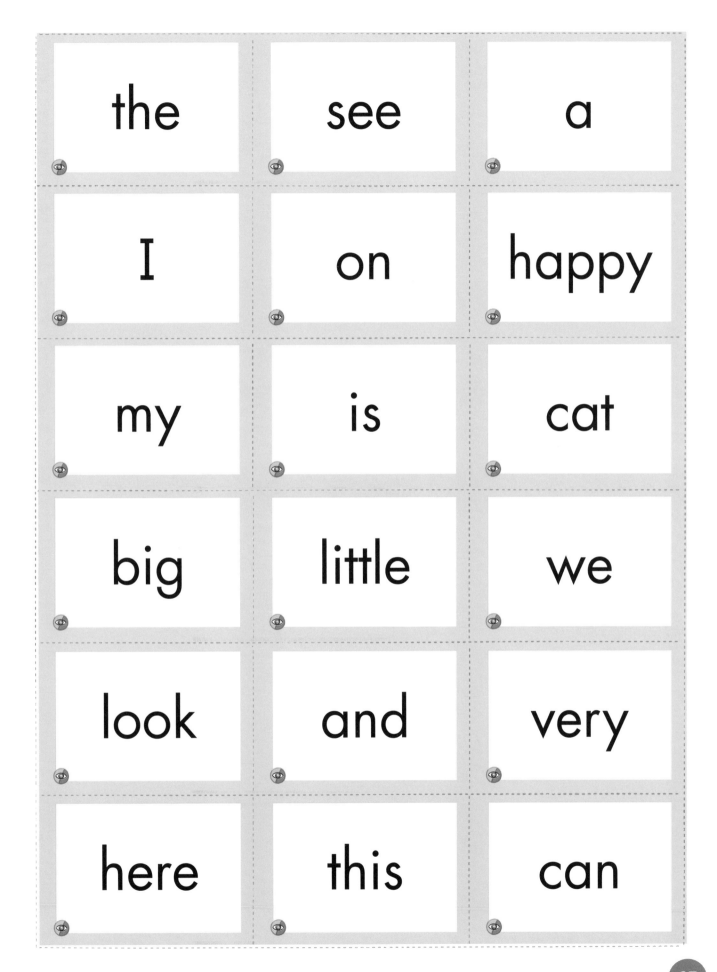

the	see	a
I	on	happy
my	is	cat
big	little	we
look	and	very
here	this	can

like	are	to
put	you	come
want	do	with
down	said	play
have	of	been
they	has	were

from	does	any
there	was	who
good	into	your
saw	find	now
our	as	her
many	under	his

one	yellow	about
two	funny	some
three	pretty	other
four	soon	give
what	know	again
away	please	would

at	am	mat
Sam	sat	fat
fast	mats	map
pan	in	Tim
an	Pam	nap
sit	man	it

sand	did	soft
not	on	in
Tom	sit	sits
hat	lost	Ed
ran	hill	doll
fell	pond	Gus

sit	band	dog
digs	on	mud
bus	in	jump
and	up	Jack
Jill	went	hill
on	jog	quack

when	duck	will
on	ship	quick
in	Rex	hat
Chad	jogs	at
fast	and	chimp
yells	jumps	ride

Jane	run	bike
mile	game	lake
Jake	can	wins
Brad	team	game
goat	eats	grass
ripe	peach	vase

Steve	rose	in
tells	Pete	joke
drives	truck	likes
can	fun	ride
June	car	blue
us		

A B C D E

F G H I J

K L M N O

P Q R S T

U V W

X Y Z

a b c d e

f g h i j

k l m n o

p q r s t

u v w

x y z

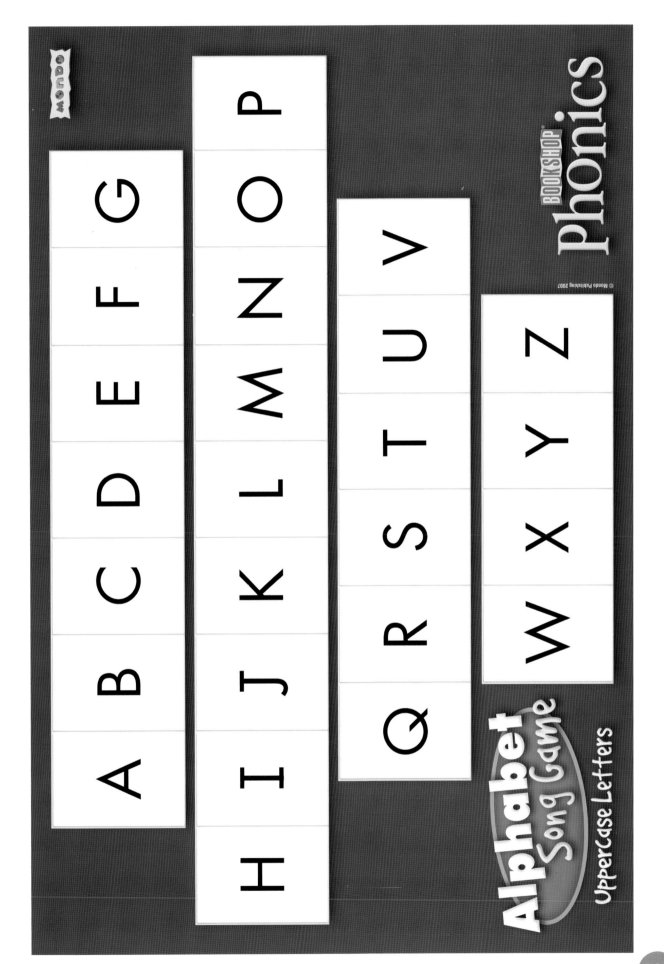

Alphabet Song Game
Uppercase Letters

A B C D E F G
H I J K L M N O P
Q R S T U V
W X Y Z

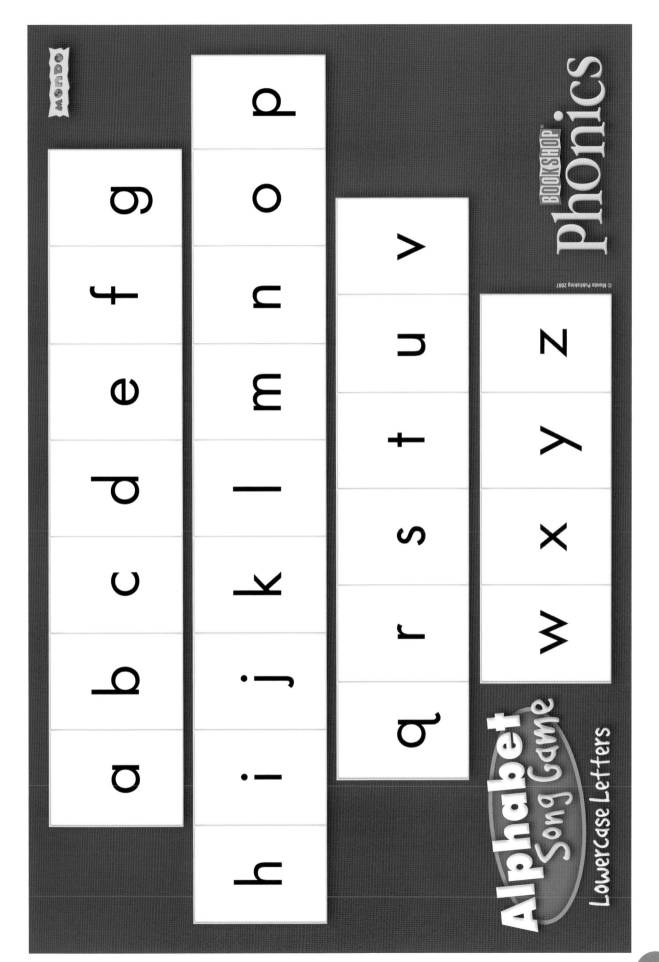

a b c d e f g

h i j k l m n o p

q r s t u v

w x y z

Alphabet Song Game
Lowercase Letters

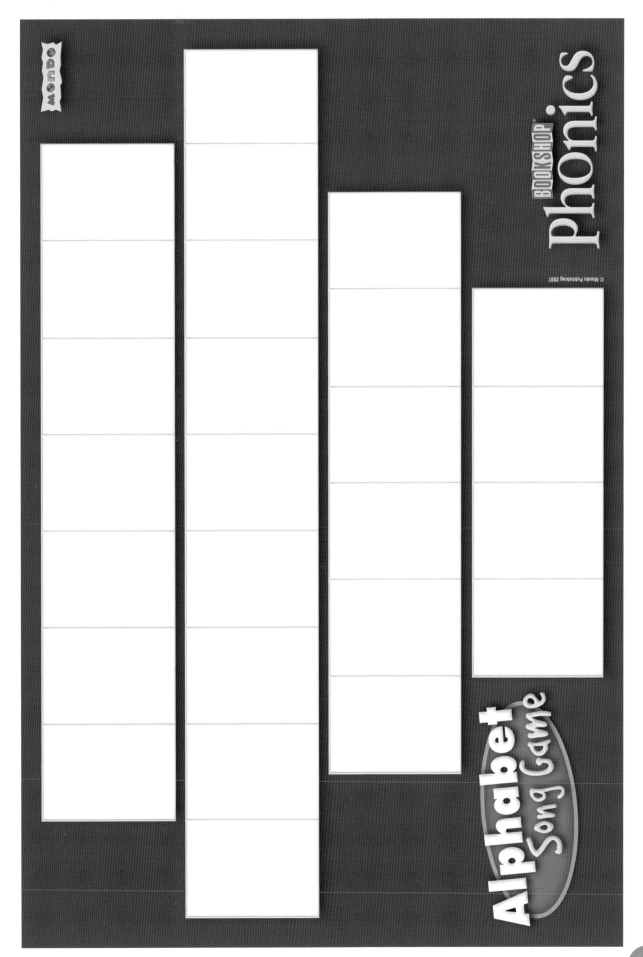

A	a	a	T	t
t	M	m	m	S
s	s	F	f	f
P	p	p	I	i
i	N	n	n	D

d d O o o

L l I R r

r H h h E

e e B b b

U u u G g

g	C	c	c	V
v	J	j	K	k
W	w	Y	y	Q
q	X	x	Z	z
sh	qu	th	ch	ai